The Legend Lurking in your Lunchbox

DINNER
DETECTIVES

First published in 2018 by
PublishCreative Books
28 Little Cleveland Street, Redfern NSW 2016, Australia

 A catalogue record for this
book is available from the
National Library of Australia

ISBN: 978-0-6480087-2-9
ISSN: 2207-2918
DDC: 823.4

Designed and typeset by Lisa Hoerlein
Printed in China

Case #103

The Legend Lurking in your Lunchbox

BY YVES STENING AND NIGEL BUCHANAN

PUBLISH + CREATIVE BOOKS

I'm Clementine and I love food. All types of food.

My little brother Aksel only eats white things,
like white bread, white rice and potatoes.

Today is a school day and that means sandwiches.

'Sandwich ... sand wich, sand witch!'
I say. 'What a funny word.'

'Sandwich?' frowns Aksel.
'A sandwich is a sandwich.'

'But why is it a sandwich?' I ask.

'Because it's bread with food!' says Aksel.

'Is cheese on toast a sandwich?' I ask.

'No,' says Aksel.

'So what's a sandwich?'

'It's got two slices of bread with bits in the middle.'

'So why isn't it called bread'n'bits?' I ask.

'Or ... a bread clamp?'

'Or a food wedge?'

'Or a food fold?' suggests Aksel.

'Or a pocket snack?'

'Or a bun crack?'

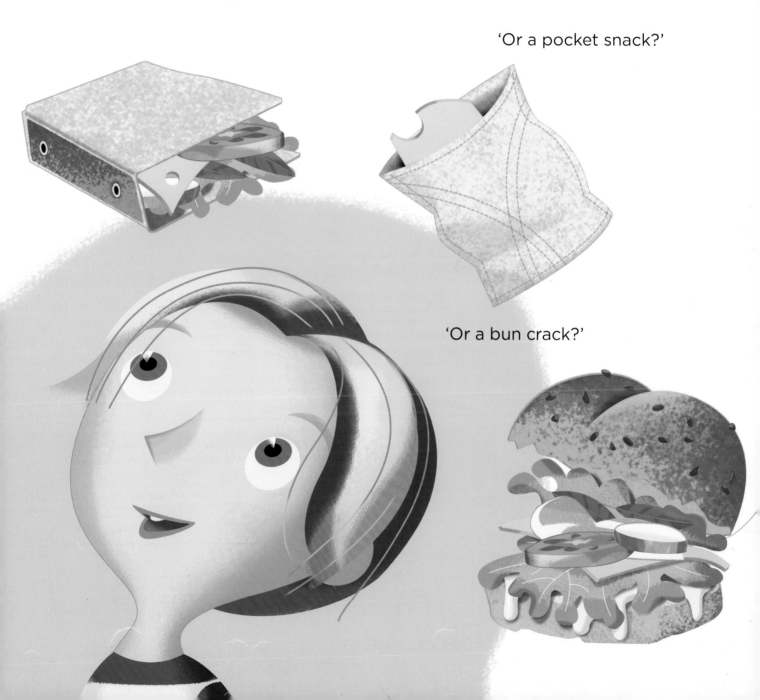

'A *bum* crack?! What would you like on your bum crack today, Aksel?'

'Honey and butter, please!'

'But why *is* it called a sandwich?' I say.

'This sounds like a case for ...'

'... the dinner detectives!'

We look up the mystery word in a big book.

'There are lots of places called Sandwich,' I tell Aksel.

'There's a town in England with a market on the beach. In the old days, markets were called "wichs", so they called the town Sandwich. Get it? Sand for the beach and wich for the market!'

'That's why witches have big hats,'
says Aksel, 'to protect them from the sun
when they're at the beach, selling potions.'

'Maybe,' I say. 'But listen to this ...'

Hundreds of years ago, the Earl of Sandwich sent
Captain James Cook on a magical journey across the seas.

'Tally ho!'

Captain Cook sailed around the world,
collecting plants and animals, observing planets,
and drawing maps of everywhere he visited.

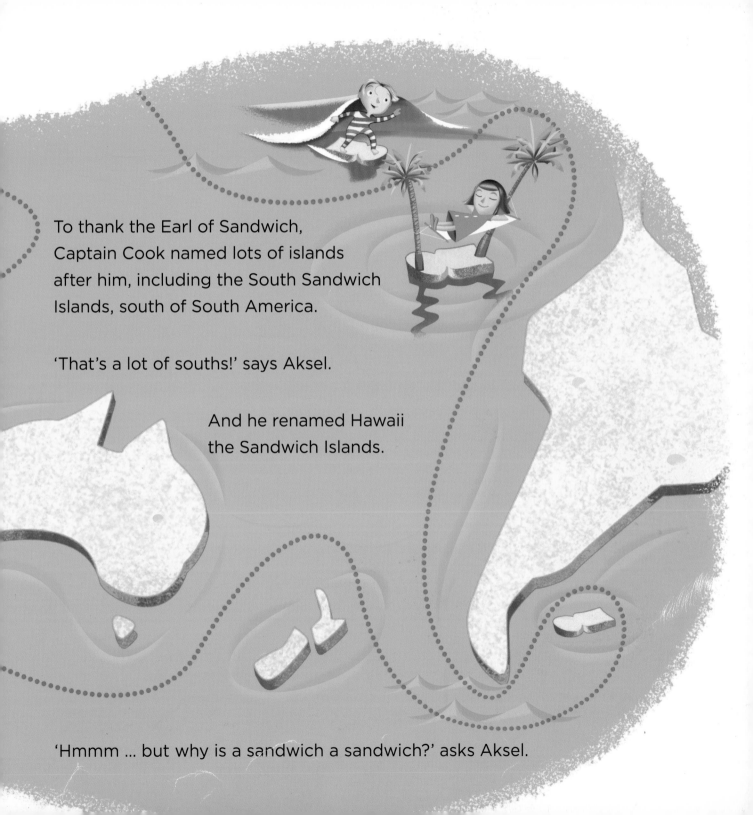

To thank the Earl of Sandwich, Captain Cook named lots of islands after him, including the South Sandwich Islands, south of South America.

'That's a lot of souths!' says Aksel.

And he renamed Hawaii the Sandwich Islands.

'Hmmm ... but why is a sandwich a sandwich?' asks Aksel.

Well, Lord Sandwich loved to play cards.
He loved it so much he would never
leave the table, not even to eat.

He told his servant, 'Bring my dinner wrapped in two slices of bread.'

If Lord Sandwich wasn't going to leave the table, neither were his friends, because ...

'He might cheat!' exclaims Aksel.

So his cook wrapped their meals in bread too.

'For Sandwich,' he told the maid.

Aksel frowns. 'So they called it a sandwich just because Lord Sandwich asked for it?'

'That's right.'

'Hear ye, hear ye! I, Sir Aksel, name bread with butter and honey …

the honey bum crack!'

'Yes, Sir Aksel, and what will you name the hamburger sandwich?'

'The hamburger sandwich?'

'Hamburg is a city in Germany.'

'Another place!' exclaims Aksel.

The people from Hamburg are called Hamburgers and they love their steak.

Hundreds of years ago, thousands of Hamburgers moved to America to work.

They weren't allowed much time for lunch, so they wrapped their steak in bread, and ate while they worked.

'Just like Lord Sandwich did!'

'Right,' I say.

'But other people must have made sandwiches before Lord Sandwich,' says Aksel.

They did.

Thousands of years ago, Hillel the Jewish sage wrapped lamb with herbs in matzo bread.

In India, they eat rotis and dosas ...

In Turkey, they eat kebabs ...

And in Mexico, they eat burritos, tacos and quesadillas, made with tortillas.

'Are they all sandwiches?' asks Aksel.

'Well, a Boston judge ruled that burritos are not sandwiches because they're made with just one tortilla, and a sandwich must have ...'

'Two slices of bread!'

'Yes! A sandwich must have two slices of bread.
Case 103 is solved by the Dinner Detectives!'

CLEMENTINE'S POACHED CHICKEN ON RYE SANDWICH

Ingredients

1 chicken breast	1 cucumber	Mayonnaise
1 teaspoon peppercorns	1/4 lemon	Light rye bread
1 bay leaf	Rocket (arugula)	Salt + ground pepper

Cook the chicken (or buy cooked chicken breast from the grocer)

Ask Dad or Mum to boil a pot of water on the stove.

Add salt, peppercorns and the bay leaf.

When the water has boiled, add your chicken breast. Put the lid on the pot, turn off the stove and leave for 25 minutes. Remove from the water.

Make the sandwich

Ask Dad or Mum to thinly slice the chicken breast, and then thinly slice some cucumber.

Add the chicken breast to a slice of rye bread. Add the cucumber, as much mayonnaise as you like, a small handful of rocket, a squeeze of lemon and a sprinkle of salt and pepper.

Throw another slice of rye bread on top.

Slice in half and serve.

My favourite sandwich is poached chicken, cucumber, rocket and mayonnaise.

It's easy to make:

1. Ask Dad or Mum to poach the chicken breast in a saucepan.

2. Ask Dad or Mum to slice the chicken breast and the cucumber.

3. Layer all the ingredients on a slice of bread. Add a squirt of mayonnaise, a pinch of salt and pepper, and a squirt of lemon.

Slice it in half and you're ready to eat.

Time to try my creation on Aksel!

'How do you like your sandwich, Aksel?'

'You mean my *bum crack*?'

'Pardon me, Sir Aksel, how do you like your bum crack?'

'After my famous *honey bum crack*,
it's my most favourite sandwich ever!'

You can share your own sandwich recipe with other Dinner Detectives at dinnerdetectives.com.au